EARTHDANCE

by Joanne Ryder

illustrated by Norman Gorbaty

SCHOLASTIC INC.
New York Toronto London Auckland Sydney

ISBN 0-590-06393-6

Text copyright © 1996 by Joanne Ryder. Illustrations copyright © 1996 by Norman Gorbaty.
All rights reserved. Published by Scholastic Inc., 555 Broadway, New York, NY 10012,
by arrangement with Henry Holt and Company, Inc.

12 11 10 9 8 7 6   1 2/0

Printed in the U.S.A.   08

First Scholastic printing, March 1997

The artist used stencils on illustration board with printing ink.

Designed by Norman Gorbaty.

For Lindsey Abdale
and all the
children of the earth
who care for it
and treasure
its creatures

— J. R.

For Joy,
who makes
my world
go round

— N. G.

Imagine
you
are
standing
tall
in
an
empty
space.

Stretch your arms out wide

and slowly spin around.

taller than the hills,

Imagine you are growing taller than the trees,

You are growing

so large, so tall

no one can see

head high in the sky.   all of you now.

Imagine you are dancing

in space, even larger than the moon.

Spinning around, you are round
wrapped in a quilt of bright colors —

blue flowing seas, dark green woods,
and deserts of golden sand.
You are twirling
so gracefully, carefully,
not even the sand
moves as you spin.

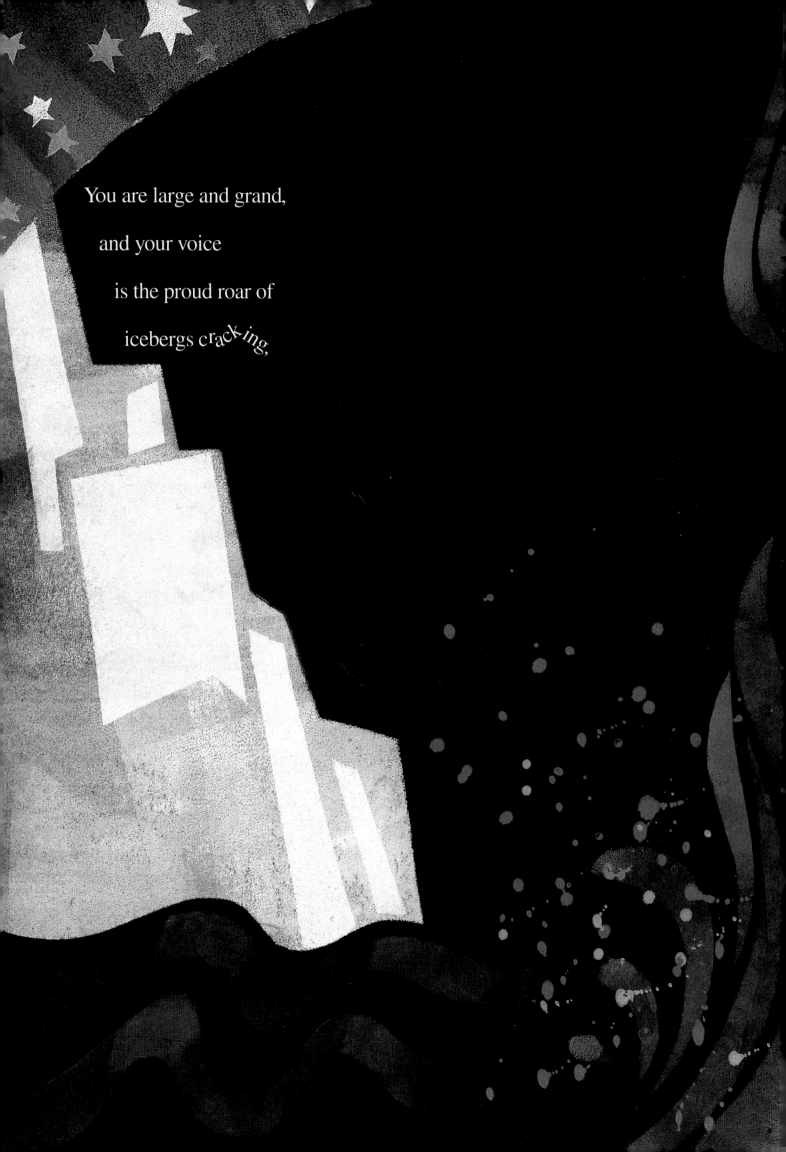

You are large and grand,

and your voice

is the proud roar of

icebergs cracking,

waterfalls tumbling.

Your whisper is a breeze murmuring through the reeds,

a tiny wave

lapping land.

Wiggle your shoulders

and

mountains

tremble

and

quake.

Shake your hair and feel windswept grasses tickle your face.

You are streaked
with roads and bridges,
spotted with farms
and factories.

Up your hills

and down your rivers,

cars and ships

carry people

from one place

to another,

all places on you.

You are where

crickets leap,

rabbits hop,

and children run and run.

Imagine
them
leaping
and
dancing
with
you
as
you
spin.

Imagine hearing them all, their voices humming as you twirl.

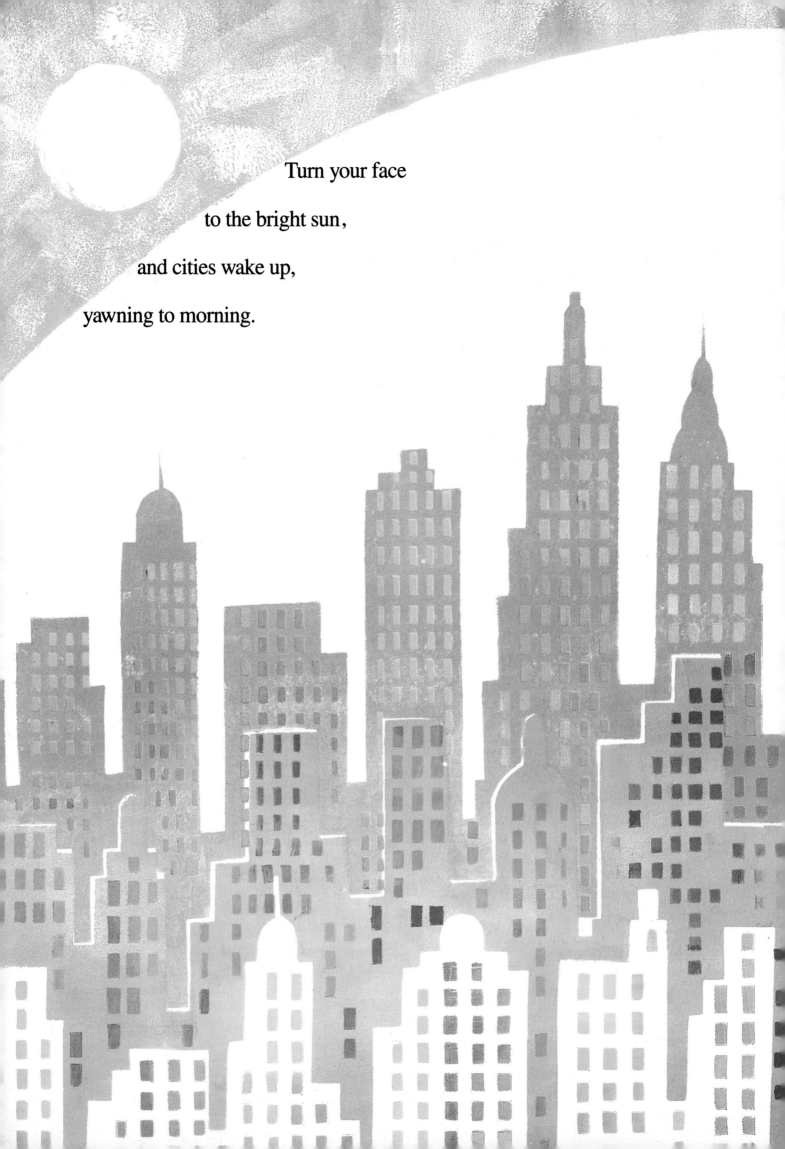

Turn your face
to the bright sun,
and cities wake up,
yawning to morning.

Behind you,

cities in darkness

turn on their lights,

go to sleep and dream.

As you spin,

you bring day

then night

to everyone

who calls you home.

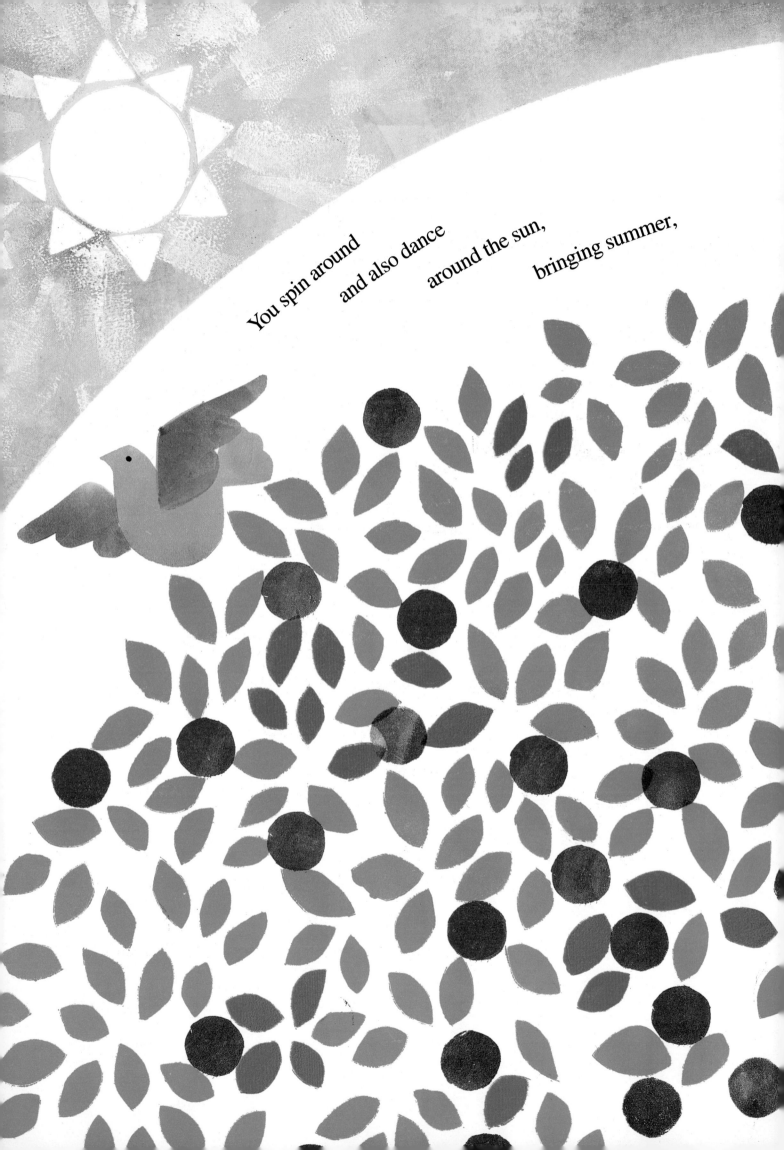

You spin around and also dance around the sun, bringing summer,

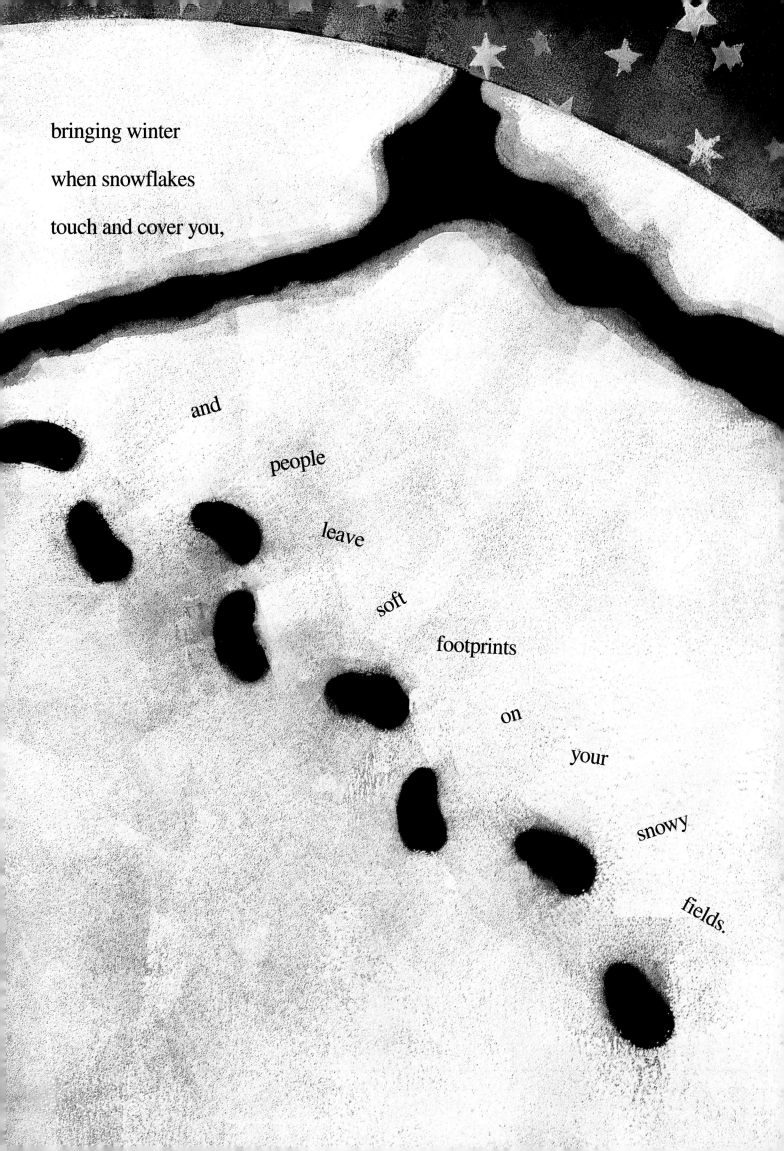

bringing winter

when snowflakes

touch and cover you,

and

people

leave

soft

footprints

on

your

snowy

fields.

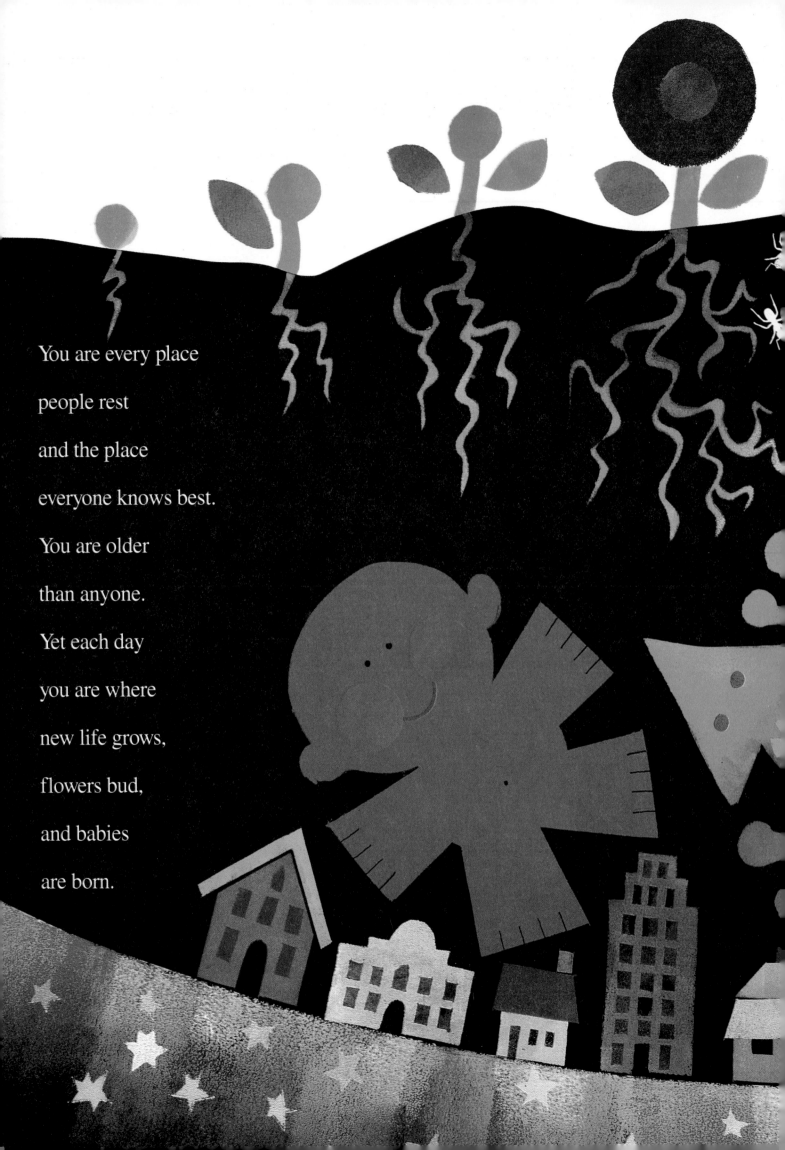

You are every place

people rest

and the place

everyone knows best.

You are older

than anyone.

Yet each day

you are where

new life grows,

flowers bud,

and babies

are born.

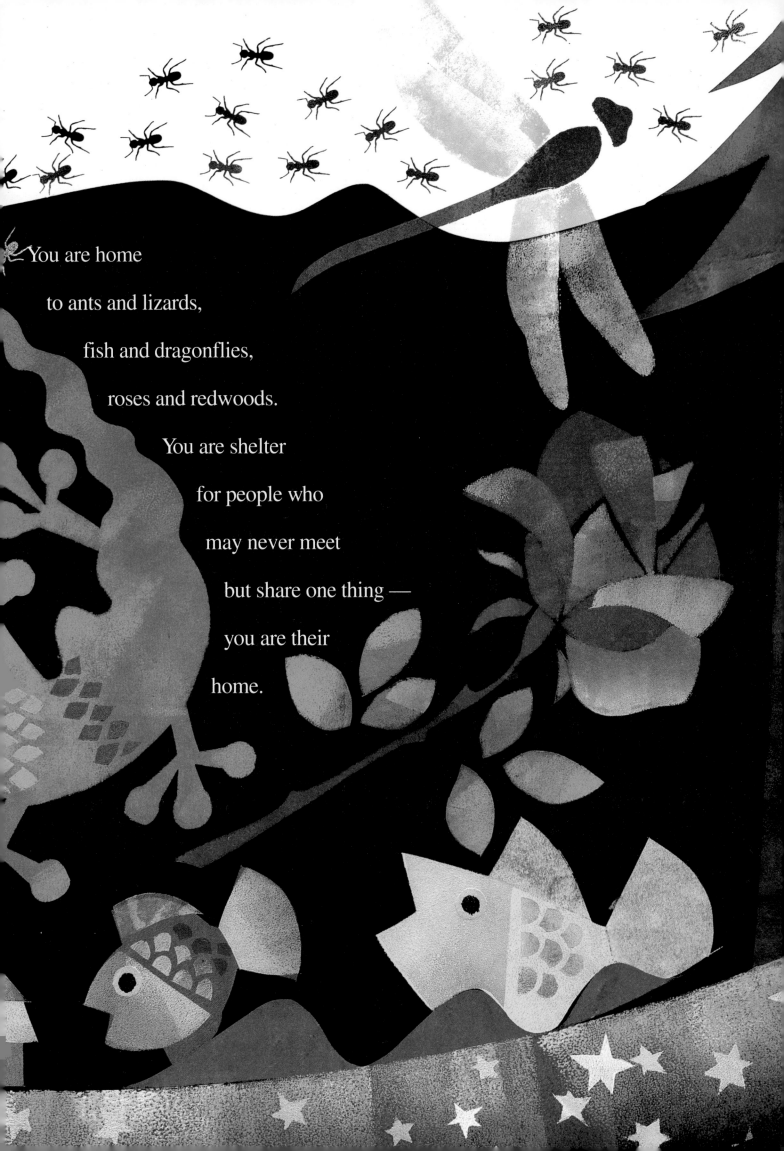

You are home

to ants and lizards,

fish and dragonflies,

roses and redwoods.

You are shelter

for people who

may never meet

but share one thing —

you are their

home.

Dance slowly,

   spin gently,

     and carry them

       through space.

May they hear

   your whispers,

     feel your strength

       under their feet,

         and treasure you.

For

you

are

home.

You

are

precious

Earth.